How to use this book

Follow the advice, in italics, given for you on each page.
Support the children as they read the text that is shaded in cream.
Praise *the children at every step!*

Detailed guidance is provided in the Read Write Inc. Phonics Handbook

9 reading activities

Children:
Practise reading the speed sounds.
Read the green, red and challenge words for the story.
Listen as you read the introduction.
Discuss the vocabulary check with you.
Read the story.
Re-read the story and discuss the 'questions to talk about'.
Read the story with fluency and expression.
Answer the questions to 'read and answer'.
Practise reading the speed words.

Speed sounds

Consonants *Say the pure sounds (do not add 'uh').*

f ff	l ll le	m mm	n nn (kn)	r rr	s ss (se)	v ve	z zz s	sh	th	ng nk

b bb	c k ck	d dd	g gg	h	j	p pp	qu	t tt	w wh	x	y	ch tch

Vowels *Say the sounds in and out of order.*

at	hen head	in	on	up	day	see happy he	high find	blow no

zoo	look	car	for door snore	fair	whirl	shout	boy spoil

*Each box contains one sound but sometimes more than one grapheme. Focus graphemes are **circled**.*

Green words

three   barn   know   cart   right   say

or   poor   sort   corn   sort   more   store   for   door

short   moor   thorn   born   sport   horse

Read in syllables.

farm`yard    →    farmyard           im`por`tant   →   important

morn`ing    →    morning            pop`corn   →   popcorn

stor`y    →    story                trans`port   →   transport

Read the root word first and then with the ending.

bore   →   bored   snort   →   snorted

ignore   →   ignored   scorn   →   scornfully

important   →   importantly

5

Red words

any o<u>the</u>r <u>tw</u>o o<u>ne</u> a<u>ll</u> h<u>er</u> <u>there</u> s<u>ai</u>d

Challenge words

<u>gue</u>ss ev<u>er</u> aft<u>er</u> f<u>ar</u>m<u>er</u>

The poor goose

Introduction

Imagine you have a friend who's a bit of a show off. What would you do if they challenged you to a race and then kept bragging they would win? Would you brag back? The goose is challenged to a race with horse and sheepdog. She can only waddle slowly so they are sure they will win. She says nothing but doesn't seem too worried.

What do you think the goose will do?

Story written by Gill Munton
Illustrated by Tim Archbold

Vocabulary check

Discuss the meaning (as used in the story) after the children have read each word.

	definition:	sentence/phrase:
chatting	talking	The three animals were chatting one morning.
snorted	blowing air through your nose	"I'm bored!" snorted the horse.
dash	run fast	Let's all dash to the end of the track.
ignored	took no notice	But the goose just ignored them.
scornfully	sneeringly	'I can't see the sheepdog,' he snorted scornfully
honked	the noise a goose makes	"I may be short," she honked.
insult	be rude	They didn't insult her any more.

Punctuation to note in this story:
1. Capital letters to start sentences and full stops to end sentences
2. Capital letters for names
3. Exclamation marks to show anger, shock and surprise
4. Apostrophe to show contractions: I'm she's don't

The poor goose

This is the story of a horse, a sheepdog, and a goose.

The three animals were chatting in the farmyard one morning.

"I'm bored!" snorted the horse.

"Let's have a bit of sport.

Let's all dash from this farmyard to the barn

at the end of the track.

I know I will get there before you two!"

The sheepdog and the goose agreed.

"I'm the fastest animal ever born,"

said the horse to himself.

"I've got long, strong legs, and I know a short cut, across the moor.

The sheepdog is not as fast as I am, and that poor goose has

no chance of winning. She's short, and fat, and silly!"

"I'm the smartest sort of animal,"

said the dog to himself.

"And I'm Farmer Popcorn's pal. He will let me

hitch a lift on his cart when he transports his sacks of corn

to the corn store in the barn.

The horse is not as smart as I am,

and that poor goose has

no chance of winning.

She's short, and fat, and silly!"

But the goose ignored them.

She just fluffed up her soft, grey wings, and didn't say anything at all.

Off they went.

The horse tore across the moor,

jumping the thorn bushes and the tree trunks.

He looked to the left and he looked to the right.

"I can't see the sheepdog,"

he snorted scornfully,

"and I can't see that silly goose!

I must be winning!"

The sheepdog hitched a lift on Farmer Popcorn's cart.

He sat on a sack of corn, grinning to himself

as the cart bumped along the track.

He looked to the left and he looked to the right.

"I can't see the horse,"

he barked importantly,

"and I can't see that silly goose.

I must be winning!"

But the goose had the best plan of all.

"I may be short," she honked,

"and I may be fat, and I may be a little bit silly.

But I have something the other two don't have!"

The goose won,

for she got to the barn door long

before the horse or the sheepdog.

After that, they didn't insult her any more.

Can you guess what the goose did?

Questions to talk about

Re-read the page. Read the question to the children. Tell them whether it is a **FIND IT** *question or* **PROVE IT** *question.*

FIND IT

✓ *Turn to the page*

✓ *Read the question*

✓ *Find the answer*

PROVE IT

✓ *Turn to the page*

✓ *Read the question*

✓ *Find your evidence*

✓ *Explain why*

Page 9: FIND IT *Why does the horse want to have a race?*

Page 10: FIND IT *Why does the horse feel sure he'll win?*

Page 11: FIND IT *What is the dog's plan?*

Page 12: PROVE IT *Why do you think the goose doesn't answer the other animals?*

Page 13: FIND IT *Why does the horse feel sure he's winning?*

Page 14: PROVE IT *Which word tells us how the dog feels?*

Page 15: PROVE IT *How does the race change?*
How do the horse and the dog feel about the goose?

Questions to read and answer

(Children complete without your help.)

1. "I'm the fastest animal ever born"
   said **the goose / the horse / the sheepdog.**

2. The sheepdog hitched a lift in the farmer's **car / van / cart.**

3. The farmer was going **to the corn store / to the shops / to the market.**

4. The sheepdog sat on **a bag of bread / a sack of corn / a sack of hay.**

5. **The horse / the sheepdog / the goose** had the best plan of all.

Speed words

farmyard	say	know	agreed	right
little	door	poor	more	sport
snorted	morning	any	anything	other
watch	their	there	now	find